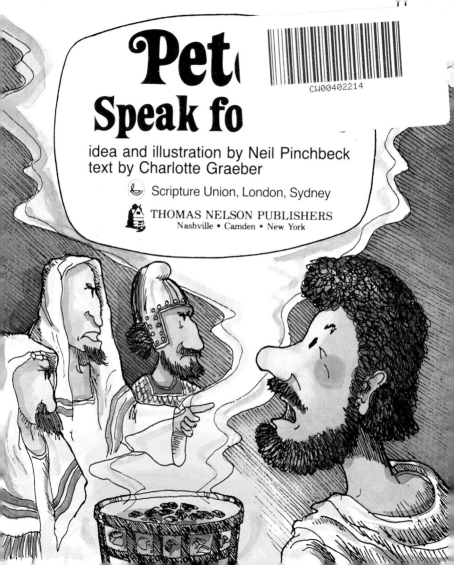

TITLES IN THIS SERIES

Moses, Speak for God!
Jonah, Speak for God
Peter, Speak for God!
Paul, Speak for God!

The Bible story is based on John chapters 18, 20 and
21 and Acts chapter 2

© Text Thomas Nelson Publishers 1986
© Illustrations Scripture Union 1986
First published in 1986

Published in the UK by Scripture Union, 130 City
Road, London EC1V 2NJ
Published in the USA by Thomas Nelson Publishers,
Nashville. Camden. New York.

ISBN 0 86201 416 6 UK
ISBN 0 85892 299 1 AUSTRALIA
ISBN 0 8407 6701 3 USA

All rights reserved. No part of this publication may be
reproduced, stored in a retrieval system, or
transmitted, in any form or by any means, electronic,
mechanical, photocopying, recording or otherwise,
without the prior permission of the publisher.

Printed by Purnell Book Production Limited.
Member of the BPCC Group, Paulton, Bristol

Sometimes Peter said words he later regretted. Before Jesus was crucified, Peter said, 'I do not know Jesus.' Once. Twice. Three times. Yet Peter was Jesus's friend.

Peter later asked himself, *Why was I such a coward*?

Then the news came! The tomb of Jesus was open and his body was gone! Peter hurried to the tomb.

He ran inside. It was true. Nothing was in the tomb but the burial cloths. Jesus had risen from the dead!

That night the disciples gathered in a secret room.
Peter still felt guilty. Why had he been a coward?

Then Jesus appeared. Peter was happy to see him alive. Still he wished he could take back the words, 'I do not know Jesus.'

Later the disciples went north. When they reached the sea, Peter said, 'Let's go fishing.'

Peter, John and the others fished all evening. They lowered their nets. Each time the nets came up empty.

All night they lowered their nets. Each time the nets came up empty. Not one small fish was caught.

At dawn a man appeared on the shore. 'Throw your nets to the right!' he called.

Peter and the others did as the man said. At once their nets filled with fish. Big fish, many fish, so many they could not pull the nets into the boat. A miracle!

Only Jesus could perform a miracle. 'Peter! It is the Lord!' John shouted.

Peter could not wait to see Jesus! SPLOSH! He jumped into the water.

SPLASH! SPLASH SPLASH! He swam to shore.

The disciples rowed the boat to shore.
   'Come and eat breakfast with me,' Jesus invited.

Later Jesus spoke to Peter. 'Peter, do you love me best?' he asked. Once. Twice. Three times.

'Yes! Yes! Yes!' Peter answered.

'Feed my sheep,' Jesus said. 'Tell everyone about me. Speak for me, Peter.'

Peter and the others began to speak in many languages – Latin, Egyptian, Arabic. 'It is the Holy Spirit!' Peter cried.

The disciples rushed into the streets. There they spoke about Jesus. Men from Rome, Egypt and Arabia understood in their own language. 'What a miracle!' they cried.

But some thought it was a trick. How could these uneducated men speak so many languages?
'They've been drinking too much wine!' they said.

Peter knew this was his chance to speak for Jesus. He would not be a coward any more. He stood in front of everyone.

'The Jesus you crucified is God's son,' Peter said.
'Now he has risen from the dead.'

The crowd grew silent. Some of them had spoken
against Jesus.

The people were sorry for what they had done. They asked Peter, 'What can we do?'

'Tell God you are sorry!' Peter said. 'Then be baptized in the name of Jesus. You, too, can receive the power of the Holy Spirit.'

What a day! Many people came forward – fifty, two hundred, a thousand! By nightfall THREE THOUSAND had been baptized, all because Peter had spoken for Jesus.

And Peter continued to speak – to Jews, to Romans, to everyone he met. Peter was no longer afraid to speak for Jesus.

Speak for God!